Dear Parents,

Welcome to the Scholastic Reader series. We have taken over 80 years of experience with teachers, parents, and children and put it into a program that is designed to match your child's interests and skills.

Level 1—Short sentences and stories made up of words kids can sound out using their phonics skills and words that are important to remember.

Level 2—Longer sentences and stories with words kids need to know and new "big" words that they will want to know.

Level 3—From sentences to paragraphs to longer stories, these books have large "chunks" of texts and are made up of a rich vocabulary.

Level 4—First chapter books with more words and fewer pictures.

It is important that children learn to read well enough to succeed in school and beyond. Here are ideas for reading this book with your child:

- Look at the book together. Encourage your child to read the title and make a prediction about the story.
- Read the book together. Encourage your child to sound out words when appropriate. When your child struggles, you can help by providing the word.
- Encourage your child to retell the story. This is a great way to check for comprehension.
- Have your child take the fluency test on the last page to check progress.

Scholastic Readers are designed to support your child's efforts to learn how to read at every age and every stage. Enjoy helping your child learn to read and love to read.

　　　　　—Francie Alexander
　　　　　Chief Education Officer
　　　　　Scholastic Education

Copyright © 1993 by Nancy Hall, Inc.
Fluency activities copyright © 2003 Scholastic Inc.
All rights reserved. Published by Scholastic Inc.
SCHOLASTIC, CARTWHEEL BOOKS, and associated logos
are trademarks and/or registered trademarks of Scholastic Inc.

Library of Congress Cataloging-in-Publication Data is available.

ISBN: 0-439-59434-0

15 14 13 12 11   10 11 12 13/0
Printed in the U.S.A. 40 • First Scholastic printing, August 1993

My Messy Room

by **Mary Packard**

Illustrated by **Stephanie Britt**

Scholastic Reader — Level 1

SCHOLASTIC INC.

New York Toronto London Auckland Sydney
Mexico City New Delhi Hong Kong Buenos Aires

I like my room messy.

It's my room. So there!

I like paint
on my table.

I like socks on my chair.

I like books on my bed.

I like toys on my floor.

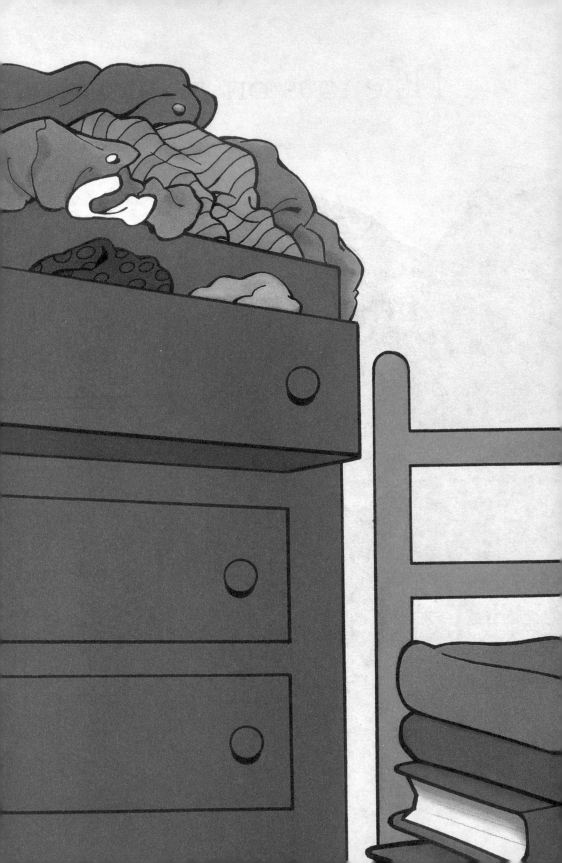

I like shirts
on my dresser.

I like shoes
in my drawer.

I like my room messy.

I like it a lot.
I like it! I like it!

But Mommy does not!

A Very Messy Room

How many things can you find that begin with the letter **s**?

Think About It

The girl in this story feels glad when her room is a mess. Her mother does not. She feels mad!

What are some things that make you feel glad?

What makes you feel mad?

What makes you feel sad?

What makes you feel bad?

Messy Sentences

The words in these sentences got all mixed up.
Can you put them back in the right order?

messy my I like room

books my like bed I on

lot like I it a

Match Them Up

Use your fingers to match the words in the row on the left with the pictures of these words on the right.

socks

table

chair

shoes

paint

books

bed

Rhyme Time

The word *locks* rhymes with the word *socks.* Can you find words in the story that rhyme with these words?

tie   not

fair   boys

broom   door

Answers

(*A Very Messy Room*)

How many things did you find that began with the letter **s**? Some of these things are:

sailboat, sandwich, saw, saxophone, scarf, schoolbag, scissors, seat, sheet, shell, shelves, ship, shirt, shoe, shorts, shovel, skate, skateboard, sled, slipper, snowsuit, spoon, stamps, stapler, stereo, stethoscope, submarine, sunglasses, sweater

Did you find any other words?

(*Think About It*)

Answers will vary.

(*Messy Sentences*)

I like my room messy.
I like books on my bed.
I like it a lot.

(*Rhyme Time*)

tie / my	not / lot
fair / chair (there)	boys / toys
broom / room	door / floor (drawer)